Amazing Animals

Edited By Jenni Harrison

First published in Great Britain in 2017 by:

Coltsfoot Drive
Peterborough
PE2 9BF
Telephone: 01733 890066
Website: www.youngwriters.co.uk

Foreword

Dear Reader,

Welcome to this book packed full of feathery, furry and scaly friends!

Young Writers' Poetry Safari competition was specifically designed for 5-7-year olds as a fun introduction to poetry and as a way to think about the world of animals. They could write about domestic pets, exotic animals or creepy crawlies! From this starting point, the poems could be as simple or as elaborate as the writer wanted, using imagination and descriptive language.

Given the young age of the entrants, we have tried to include as many poems as possible. Here at Young Writers we believe that seeing their work in print will inspire a love of reading and writing and give these young poets the confidence to develop their skills in the future. Poetry is a wonderful way to introduce young children to the idea of rhyme and rhythm and helps learning and development of communication, language and literacy skills.

These young poets have used their creative writing abilities, sentence structure skills, thoughtful vocabulary and most importantly, their imaginations, to make their poems and the animals within them come alive. I hope you enjoy reading them as much as we have.

Jenni Harrison

Contents

St Patrick's Primary School, Omagh

Aine Corrigan (6)	61
Joshua Watson (7)	62
Ciabhan Kilpatrick (7)	63
Rosa McNulty (6)	64
Chloe Ann Patton (6)	65
Finn Wolfe (7)	66
William David Devine (6)	67
Conor Doherty (6)	68

St Peter's RC Primary School, Leicester

Adiena Evans (5)	69
Ethan Shenton (6)	70
Anthony Majewski (5)	71
Isabella Allen (5)	72
Noah White (5), Grace Sanders (5) & Ethan Thomas Wale (5)	73
Jacob Wright (5)	74
Isabelle Wood (5)	75
Millie Neale (5)	76
Isaac Abela Georg (6)	77
Will Hall (6)	78
Alfie Hewkin (6)	79
Serena Pagliari (6)	80
Isla Lapsley (6)	81
Ella-Daisy Braidley (6)	82
TJ Bhatt (7)	83
Lily Grace Cooper (6)	84
Darcey Rai Morgan (6)	85
Finn Cameron Eyles (6)	86
Charlie Longman (6)	87
Zaine Barden (6)	88
Jessica Wann (6)	89
Oliver Burton (6)	90

Tír-Na-Nóg Primary School, Ballyclare

Emily Lecky (8)	91
Oliver Graham (7)	92

Caitlin Wylie (6)	93
Faith Sole (6)	94
Calvin Kirkpatrick (7)	95

The Glasgow Academy Dairsie, Glasgow

Murray D H Thomson (7)	96
Harry Farquharson (7)	97
Kenneth Ou (7)	98
Eilidh Reid	99
Sebastian Carmichael (7)	100
Dominic Murray (6)	101

Tong Primary School, Isle Of Lewis

Rosie Eleanor Fletcher (7)	102
Daniel France (6)	104
Dylan MacDonald (7)	105
Leah Macritchie (7)	106
Joe Murray (7)	107
David Finlayson (8)	108
Amelia Mackay (6)	109
Ruben Matheson (8)	110
Johan Tynan (7)	111
Jayden Pidcock (7)	112
Jayden Maciver (7)	113

Torphichen Primary School, Bathgate

Marcus Miller (5)	114
Martin Miller (5)	115
Lilly Campbell (6)	116
Alison Baird (6)	117
Finn McMorrow (6)	118
Layla Rose Thomson (6)	119
Libby Fisher (6)	120
Summer Dunsmore (5)	121

Watlington Community Primary School, King's Lynn

Ollie Saw (6)	122
Naomi Gelder (6)	123
Imogen Coote (6)	124
Dylan Whiting (7)	125
Rhys Loveday (6)	126
Harry Richard Gorringe (6)	127
Erin-Ruby Patricia Cooke (6)	128
Libby Hope Johnson (6)	129
Ava Faith Brooks (6)	130
Alfie Summers (6)	131
Harrison Cannon (6)	132
Finlay Dix (6)	133
Maisie Baker (6)	134
Macy Jordan (6)	135
Samuel Mills (6)	136
Leo Sillis (6)	137
Benjamin Buck (6)	138
Isabelle Pearman (6)	139
Theo Sanderson (6)	140

The Poems

The Gorilla

I hear the trees swing as the gorilla
eats silently.
I see him walking around looking for food.
He is very silent.
And really lonely.
A hairy gorilla sits upon a rock
And watches the world go by.
He watches silently.
I can taste fur.
I feel his hair, it is furry.
I can see him eating.
I can hear his young.
I see him go to sleep silently.

Amelie Wall (6)
Alderley Edge Community Primary School, Alderley Edge

Elephant

An enormous, colossal elephant.
A grey, big, cross elephant.
It has a long, swishy tail.
It is longer than its trunk.
It has big, massive, long legs.
Its head is like a rhino's.
Because it's as strong as a hammer.
Fascinating, stinky, colossal elephant.
It has big, beady eyes.
Big, terrifying elephant.
A hungry, thirsty elephant.

Amelia Karlsson-Smyth (6)

Alderley Edge Community Primary School, Alderley Edge

The Snake Poem

I see a smooth, patterned snake.
I hear it slithering through the crunchy,
green leaves.
It smells of sweet-smelling roses.
Its eyes are camouflaged to its skin.
It likes to eat muddy, squiggly worms.
And it also likes to eat black, shiny ants.

Abigail Sophia Fairbrother (6)
Alderley Edge Community Primary School, Alderley Edge

The Elephant Poem

My animal is a grey elephant.
Its ears are as big as a table.
Its legs are as strong as a hammer.
And its trunk is as long as a roller coaster.
As well as *stomp, stomp, stomp!*

Aston Lee (6)
Alderley Edge Community Primary School, Alderley Edge

My Gorilla Poem

My gorilla is as strong as a lion.
My gorilla is as loud as a lion.
My gorilla is as fat as a lion.
My gorilla is as bony as a lion.
My gorilla is as stinky as a lion.

Marley Oakes (6)
Alderley Edge Community Primary School, Alderley Edge

The Giraffe

I woke up one morning.
I smelt egg.
I love the smell of egg.
But my egg was not there.
Where could it be?
I love my eggs.
Bad news! A giraffe ate it!

Ava Lloyd-Jones (6)
Alderley Edge Community Primary School, Alderley Edge

Lion

I saw colossal, sharp teeth!
It smelt terrific.
It had fluffy ears.
It had little eyes.
A fierce mane.
A pointed tail.
The lion ran and ran.

Dylan George Aston (6)
Alderley Edge Community Primary School, Alderley Edge

The Cheetah

I feel his thin fur.
I hear wind when he sprints around.
I see a wet nose and beady eyes,
I taste a bony body.
I smell sweat running down his face.

Rocky Maguire (7)
Alderley Edge Community Primary School, Alderley Edge

A Leopard

It smells hairy and smelly.
It feels smooth and very soft.
It looks brown and spotty.
It tastes hairy and horrible.
It sounds loud and roary.

Dawud Zaydan Ahmed (6)
Alderley Edge Community Primary School, Alderley Edge

The Lion

A roaring, yellow lion.
I see a lion.
I taste fur.
Purr, purr, purr.
Sharp claws.
Ferocious lion.
Stomping paws.

Luka Sedej-Dobrun (7)
Alderley Edge Community Primary School, Alderley Edge

The Lion Poem

I see a fluffy, silky, soft lion.
I smell a strong smell from the lion.
I hear a loud roar from the lion.
I can feel a smooth lion.

Elissia Smith (6)
Alderley Edge Community Primary School, Alderley Edge

Zebra

It feels silky and soft.
It smells like the jungle.
I hear stomping.
A big, colossal tail.
Swish, swish.

Ellie Green (6)
Alderley Edge Community Primary School, Alderley Edge

A Bunny Poem

A bunny is as soft as a bed.
As bouncy as a horse.
As hairy as a dog.
As bony as a cheetah.
As furry as a bush.

Mason Byrom (6)
Alderley Edge Community Primary School, Alderley Edge

Cheetah

My cheetah feels dirty.
My cheetah smells dusty.
My cheetah tastes meaty.
My cheetah looks spotty.
My cheetah sounds quiet.
My cheetah feels soft.
My cheetah smells stinky.
My cheetah tastes nice.
My cheetah sounds stompy.
My cheetah feels cuddly.

Tyrone Nyangweso (6)
Dunard Primary School, Glasgow

Cheetah

My cheetah feels soft.
My cheetah smells awesome.
My cheetah tastes like chicken.
My cheetah looks whiskery
and like a cat and spotty.
My cheetah sounds sneaky.

Amber Sarah McGlynn (6)
Dunard Primary School, Glasgow

Cheetah

My cheetah feels fluffy.
My cheetah smells awesome.
My cheetah tastes like chicken.
My cheetah looks whiskery
And like a cat.
My cheetah sounds sneaky.

Fiza Nasir (7)
Dunard Primary School, Glasgow

Cheetah

My cheetah feels soft
My cheetah smells stinky
My cheetah looks spotty
My cheetah tastes like chicken
My cheetah sounds stompy.

Steven Tshinyoka (7)
Dunard Primary School, Glasgow

Cheetah

My cheetah feels dirty.
My cheetah smells dusty.
My cheetah looks hairy.
My cheetah tastes horrible.
My cheetah sounds sneaky.

Alexander Bryce Macdonald (5)
Dunard Primary School, Glasgow

Dolphin

Dolphins taste fishy.
Dolphins smell like seaweed.
Dolphins look beautiful.
Dolphins sound like splashing.
Dolphins feel wet.

Hope MacGillivrey (6)
Dunard Primary School, Glasgow

Cheetah

My cheetah feels soft.
My cheetah smells dusty.
My cheetah tastes delicious.
My cheetah looks spotty.
My cheetah sounds loud.

Artian Lushaku (7)
Dunard Primary School, Glasgow

Hyenas

Hyenas taste disgusting.
Hyenas smell hairy.
Hyenas look spotty and yellow.
Hyenas sound scary and loud.
Hyenas feel fluffy.

Morgan Schad-Burn (6)
Dunard Primary School, Glasgow

Cheetah

My cheetah feels soft
My cheetah tastes delicious
My cheetah smells sweaty
My cheetah sounds sneaky
My cheetah looks spotty.

Treasure Thomas (6)
Dunard Primary School, Glasgow

Cheetah

My cheetah feels soft.
My cheetah smells dusty.
My cheetah tastes yucky.
My cheetah looks spotty.
My cheetah sounds sneaky.

Abbie Doyle (7)
Dunard Primary School, Glasgow

Cheetah

My cheetah feels soft
My cheetah smells sweaty
My cheetah tastes yucky
My cheetah looks spotty
My cheetah sounds quiet.

Aaron McGinlay (7)
Dunard Primary School, Glasgow

Rabbits

Rabbits taste yucky and furry.
Rabbits feel fluffy.
Rabbits look cute.
Rabbits smell beautiful.
Rabbits sound quiet.

Kayleigh Macdonald (6)
Dunard Primary School, Glasgow

Cheetah

Cheetah tastes bony.
Cheetah smells soggy.
Cheetah looks skinny.
Cheetah sounds fierce.
Cheetah feels hairy.

Olivia Brydson (6)
Dunard Primary School, Glasgow

Cheetah

Cheetahs taste meaty.
Cheetahs smell smelly.
Cheetahs look lovely.
Cheetahs sound loud.
Cheetahs feel soft.

Fatima Mobasher (6)
Dunard Primary School, Glasgow

Anaconda

Anaconda tastes nice
Anaconda smells pongy
Anaconda looks scary
Anaconda sounds hissy
Anaconda feels slimy.

Callum Jackson (6)
Dunard Primary School, Glasgow

Turkey

Turkeys taste yummy.
Turkeys smell yummy.
Turkeys look cute.
Turkeys sound scary.
Turkeys feel feathery.

Adam Muir (5)
Dunard Primary School, Glasgow

Untitled

Leopards taste like meat.
Leopards smell lovely.
Leopards look dotty.
Leopards sound like *grr, grr*.

Annabella Quirk (6)
Dunard Primary School, Glasgow

Untitled

Zebras taste yucky.
Zebras smell pongy.
Zebras look stripy.
Zebras sound noisy.
Zebras feel fluffy.

Rosie O'Brien (6)
Dunard Primary School, Glasgow

Untitled

Snakes taste yucky.
Snakes smell stinky.
Snakes look scary.
Snakes sound grumpy.
Snakes feel slimy.

Kyle Hutcheson (6)
Dunard Primary School, Glasgow

Pandas

Pandas taste meaty.
Pandas smell flowery.
Pandas look cute.
Pandas sound roary.
Pandas feel soft.

Maisie Walker (6)
Dunard Primary School, Glasgow

Spooky Tarantulas

Tarantulas taste yucky.
Tarantulas are disgusting.
Tarantulas are scary.
Tarantulas like nothing.

Millie Houriez (6)
Dunard Primary School, Glasgow

Untitled

Cheetah tastes chewy.

Cheetah smells pongy.

Cheetah looks like a jungle.

Cheetah feels fluffy.

Rebecca Agnes Joan Canero (5)
Dunard Primary School, Glasgow

White Bear

It went to a playpark
And went with his friends.
It likes to swim in the water.
If fish are about,
They'd better watch out
Or they will be for supper!

On an icy island,
Mountains he will climb,
To stand
And stare
At the land around.

Freya Alexander (6)
Fishermoss School, Aberdeen

My Pet Cat

She is pink and purple and a happy cat!
She eats lots of mice and is quite fat.
The mice run quite fast
She can't always last...
To catch them.

She is happy and purrs
With toys that are hers
And cheers me up
Sometimes!

Kelechukwu Nwokoloh (6)
Fishermoss School, Aberdeen

My Elephant!

My elephant is grey
He eats lots and lots of leaves
He eats lots and lots of hay

He walks slowly around
His trunk near the ground
Sniffing for food.

In the pool
Fun is the rule
Squirting water all around.

Charlie Wilson
Fishermoss School, Aberdeen

The Boy And The Hungry Lion

It was a stormy day
A boy was out to play
He was caught in the rain
And ran to the cave
Not knowing the lion was in
He was not so brave
He was chased away
And the lion went back
To his cave.

Hiro Wanchoo (6)
Fishermoss School, Aberdeen

Scaly The Fish

He swims in a tank
He eats fish food
He has scales
He thinks playing is good
And friends he should thank
For playing his games
And not calling names
Although...
He is a queer shape!

Ryan Lawrie (6)
Fishermoss School, Aberdeen

Hamish The Haggis

Hamish is yellow
With a tartan hat
He had his toast
Watched by a cat.

He set off in his car
To go quite far
To Loch Ness to find
The monster, Nessie
Or another kind.

Daniel Young (5)
Fishermoss School, Aberdeen

The Cazebra

She is half cat
And half zebra.
She is black and white
With stripes.

She likes to run fast
She likes sliding down hills
She likes green
Because it is like the grass.

Ivy Matthew (5)
Fishermoss School, Aberdeen

Cheeky Monkey

She climbs trees.
She scoffs bananas.
She is cuddly and brown.
She likes bananas.
She plays with her friends.
She loves bananas!
She goes for a swing.
She has a sore tummy!

Megan Marshall (5)
Fishermoss School, Aberdeen

Sophie The Cat

My cat is called Sophie
She likes to play in my garden
She likes to eat fish and drink milk
She likes to chase flies
And then she cries
When there is no milk
In her dish!

Obuma Edema (6)
Fishermoss School, Aberdeen

The Naughty Tiger

One day
He bit an elephant
The elephant went
Stamp! Stamp! Stamp!
And chased the tiger
Home to the cave
And he...
Shook! Shook! Shook!

Michael Ani (6)
Fishermoss School, Aberdeen

Lucky Oreo Cat

Oreo climbed the tree
She was stuck!
Her owner
Caught her when she fell
She was lucky
Selena gave her some cat food
Oreo ran off to chase a mouse.

Nikita Ray (6)
Fishermoss School, Aberdeen

The Bunny

My bunny
Is funny
She sits
And twitches her nose!
She sits up smart
For carrots she loves
And runs round the garden
Like a galloping horse.

Hayley Anderson (6)
Fishermoss School, Aberdeen

Slithering Snake

He slithers around
Over the ground
Through the grass
Moving quite fast!

He moves around
And food is found
Delicious worms and bugs.

Ritchie J Horne (6)
Fishermoss School, Aberdeen

Crazy Leopard

He runs crazy fast
He wins five races
He runs to the stream
He swims crazy fast
He climbs crazy fast
He never comes last
Now he is fast asleep!

Tyler Webster (6)
Fishermoss School, Aberdeen

The Crazy Elephant

He is really very funny
And is the champion drinker
He loves to play and eat
But is not a thinker
He gets stuck in the bars
And doesn't get far!

Liam McShane
Fishermoss School, Aberdeen

Panda Bear

It likes to climb trees
And eats bamboo
It is black and white
It lives in China
And there are not many left
So we should try
To protect them!

Kayleigh Ramsay (6)
Fishermoss School, Aberdeen

Jack

Jack likes cat food
Jack likes to play
He lives with a family
He is very happy
They are very nice
He is able to catch all the mice!

Aston Crawford
Fishermoss School, Aberdeen

My Donkey

Once my donkey was in the cold winter
No one would come
To take him to get food
Or
To get warm
And cosy
Only an old dog.

Lorna McLean (6)

Fishermoss School, Aberdeen

The Giraffe Crocodile

Tall as a tree
Yellow and green
Big smile
Wiggly ears
Off he strolls
To the river
To find juicy leaves
And apples.

Cal Rowe (5)
Fishermoss School, Aberdeen

The Spider

He likes to hang upside down
To catch his flies
And wrap them, yum
And then moves home
To other houses
It's such fun!

Bailey Cran (6)
Fishermoss School, Aberdeen

The Lion

My yellow lion lives in a zoo
He is scary too!
He likes to run
And eat fish
And going down the slide
Is his biggest wish.

Reiss Mitchell (6)
Fishermoss School, Aberdeen

The Silly Monkey

She gets bananas easily from trees
She loves to swim in the river
She lives in a hot, hot box
She eats lots and lots of bananas.

Wojciech Wtorkiewicz (6)
Fishermoss School, Aberdeen

The Snake

He is very sneaky
He likes to explore the jungle
He has food to eat
And he might meet
An elephant!

Caelan Saville (5)
Fishermoss School, Aberdeen

Life In The Zoo

He lives in a zoo
He eats bamboo
He is quite rare
We try not to scare
Him.

Aiden Ryan Zanre (6)
Fishermoss School, Aberdeen

Snake Fun

He likes slithering
He feels soft
He likes the park
He likes frogs.

Rebecca Ogg (6)
Fishermoss School, Aberdeen

Mrs Hop

Fluffy and soft
And likes to hop and jump
Likes to burrow
Likes to eat carrots
And green grass
Happy and cheerful
She's a rabbit.

Aine Corrigan (6)
St Patrick's Primary School, Omagh

Mike The Turtle

Turtles are cool and they're so wet
But Mike is better, he loves water
He likes to play, he is brave
And he brushes his teeth with a leaf.

Joshua Watson (7)
St Patrick's Primary School, Omagh

Three-Horned Joe

Three-horned Joe
Caring as a bear
Likes to play ball
And doesn't play fair
An orange leg
A red knee
Black horns, 1, 2, 3.

Ciabhan Kilpatrick (7)
St Patrick's Primary School, Omagh

Bailey

Follows my mummy
Looking so proud
Sits on the sofa
When he's not allowed
He barks at the postman
And when there's a crowd.

Rosa McNulty (6)
St Patrick's Primary School, Omagh

Coco

Coco follows Daddy
Chases after rabbits
Always happy
Always playful
Water is where he likes to be
I love Coco.

Chloe Ann Patton (6)
St Patrick's Primary School, Omagh

Mr Biggy

All day long,
Mr Biggy eats fish and leaves,
Mr Biggy loves going in the water every day
To get some fish.

Finn Wolfe (7)
St Patrick's Primary School, Omagh

Tiger Tiger

He looks like Mum
But not like Dad.
She is so good
And he is so bad.
He eats people.

William David Devine (6)
St Patrick's Primary School, Omagh

Tim Pteradactyl

A big pterodactyl
He loves to get frozen
He loves to eat fish
He is dangerous.

Conor Doherty (6)
St Patrick's Primary School, Omagh

Animals

A lligators have sharp teeth

N arwhals are ice breakers

I mpalas are good fighters

M onkeys are good swingers

A nteaters are very good at sniffing ants

L ions are very good hunters

S nakes are good slitherers.

Adiena Evans (5)

St Peter's RC Primary School, Leicester

Animals

A lligators have sharp teeth
N arwhals are the best swimmers
I mpalas are high jumpers
M onkeys are banana eaters
A nteaters have a long tongue
L ions are loud roarers
S nakes can slither.

Ethan Shenton (6)
St Peter's RC Primary School, Leicester

Animals

A lligators have sharp teeth

N arwhals have long, pointy horns

I mpalas are plant eaters

M onkeys have funny faces

A nteaters have tiny ears

L ions eat meat

S nakes have forked tongues.

Anthony Majewski (5)

St Peter's RC Primary School, Leicester

Animals

A lligators are meat eaters
N arwhals are fast swimmers
I mpalas are good fighters
M onkeys are swingers
A nteaters are furry
L ions are loud roarers
S nakes are hissers.

Isabella Allen (5)

St Peter's RC Primary School, Leicester

Animals

A lligators have a long tail
N arwhals have a pointy nose
I mpalas jump high
M onkeys eat bananas
A nteaters have long tongues
L ions roar
S nakes slither.

Noah White (5), Grace Sanders (5) & Ethan Thomas Wale (5)
St Peter's RC Primary School, Leicester

Animals

A lligators wait
N arwhals have a pointy horn
I mpalas jump high
M onkeys eat bananas
A nteaters have a very long tongue
L ions roar
S nakes slither.

Jacob Wright (5)
St Peter's RC Primary School, Leicester

Animals

A lligators eat meat

N arwhals swim underwater

I mpalas have horns

M onkeys eat bananas

A nteaters eat meat

L ions eat meat

S nakes are loud hissers.

Isabelle Wood (5)

St Peter's RC Primary School, Leicester

Animals

A lligators snap
N arwhals have a long nose
I mpalas jump
M onkeys eat bananas
A nteaters run
L ions roar
S nakes slither.

Millie Neale (5)
St Peter's RC Primary School, Leicester

Whale

A big biter
A tail wagger
A belly flopper
A wave maker
A high diver
A good explorer
A sea crasher.

Isaac Abela Georg (6)
St Peter's RC Primary School, Leicester

Spider

A fierce biter.
A creepy crawler.
An angry bear.
A fierce prowler.
A scary jumper.
A creepy shadow.

Will Hall (6)
St Peter's RC Primary School, Leicester

Snake

A fast chomper
A creepy crawler
A tree climber
An exceilent climber
A night lurker
A long biter.

Alfie Hewkin (6)
St Peter's RC Primary School, Leicester

Lion

A fast runner
A loud howler
A fierce hunter
A sharp chomper
A meat eater
A ferocious fighter.

Serena Pagliari (6)
St Peter's RC Primary School, Leicester

Fish

A cute creature
A daring explorer
A scary biter
A sneaky eater
A big splasher
A fish gobbler.

Isla Lapsley (6)
St Peter's RC Primary School, Leicester

Snake

An egg layer
A tree climber
A shadow pouncer
A slimy hugger
A slow slitherer
A fast gobbler.

Ella-Daisy Braidley (6)
St Peter's RC Primary School, Leicester

Whale

A big splasher
A sea explorer
A scary biter
A big splasher
A deadly eater
A good hunter.

T J Bhatt (7)

St Peter's RC Primary School, Leicester

Whale

A giant gobbler
A wave maker
A sea crasher
A deep diver
A fast swimmer
A belly flopper.

Lily Grace Cooper (6)
St Peter's RC Primary School, Leicester

Spider

A web spinner
A man biter
Sharp jaws
A good mother
A good tickler
A good hunter.

Darcey Rai Morgan (6)
St Peter's RC Primary School, Leicester

Lion

A fast hunter
A cool splasher
A meat eater
A fierce hunter
A ferocious roarer.

Finn Cameron Eyles (6)
St Peter's RC Primary School, Leicester

Bird

A sky glider
An egg layer
A tree pecker
A noisy chatterer
A noisy creature.

Charlie Longman (6)
St Peter's RC Primary School, Leicester

Bird

A deep swimmer
A sneaky eater
A deep diver
A big splasher
A fast swimmer.

Zaine Barden (6)
St Peter's RC Primary School, Leicester

Whale

A big biter
A fast swimmer
A good explorer
A sea diver
A sea glider.

Jessica Wann (6)
St Peter's RC Primary School, Leicester

Bird

A liver
A noisy chatter
An egg grabber
A fierce hunter
A glider.

Oliver Burton (6)
St Peter's RC Primary School, Leicester

The Cute Little Puppy

Puppies are lively like a children's cartoon
Bouncy and mad like monkeys at the zoo
My new little puppy is as golden as a
toffee sweet
And as rich as homemade caramel sauce
She is as lovely as the most precious ruby
And as cute as a button
Some puppies are as lively and as funny as
a good comedian
My puppy is silly like a goose and as happy
as a clown
Some puppies are sleepy like a koala bear
hanging from the tree
My puppy is always snoozing.

Emily Lecky (8)
Tír-Na-Nóg Primary School, Ballyclare

All About Tarantulas

The scary tarantula is as fierce as a
drooling lion
And as hungry as a fast wolf out hunting
Many tarantulas are large like an elephant
Many smaller like a mouse
To hide from their prey
The sly tarantulas are as smart as owls in
the woods at night
They pounce and grip onto their prey
Like a strong, bold ox
Tarantulas are hairy like an ape
The stinging hair protects them
Like spikes of a hedgehog.

Oliver Graham (7)
Tír-Na-Nóg Primary School, Ballyclare

The Wild Lion

A lion is as brave as a superhero
A lion is as strong as a
champion weightlifter
A lion can hunt like a huntsman
A lion can roar as loud as thunder
A lion's mane is fluffy as a sheep
Lions range in colour like a golden puppy
A wild lion looks as free as a bird
A zoo lion looks trapped like a
puppy in his cage.

Caitlin Wylie (6)
Tír-Na-Nóg Primary School, Ballyclare

The Fast Cheetah

The cheetah is as fast as a racing car
Cheetahs can hunt food like a huntsman
A cheetah can jump as long as a bus
My cheetah is as spotty as the chicken pox
A cheetah can climb like a monkey
A cheetah's tail is as long as a rope
I love cheetahs because they are as
fast as lightning.

Faith Sole (6)
Tír-Na-Nóg Primary School, Ballyclare

The Fiercest Tiger

Tigers are like superheroes
The way they run
They are as fierce as a lion
Tigers are as tough as nails
Tigers sneak up onto their prey
Like a shooting rocket.

Calvin Kirkpatrick (7)
Tír-Na-Nóg Primary School, Ballyclare

Bruno The Dog

My dog is a Labrador
He sleeps next to a wine fridge!
He is twelve years old and I have known him
all my life
When he gets out of his bed he slobbers
We lift him into the car because he is old
Our car needs air freshener because Bruno
is smelly
Old, slow and smelly, but we love him.

Murray D H Thomson (7)
The Glasgow Academy Dairsie, Glasgow

Alfie

Alfie is cute, he runs around
He likes to play and snooze and frown
He trots along and wiggles and chats
He snuggles in the car and jumps
out with glee
He eats his food, plays in the garden and
jumps around
Alfie is my favourite dog
I love it when he comes to visit.

Harry Farquharson (7)
The Glasgow Academy Dairsie, Glasgow

Cloud The Cat

Cloud is my friend's cat
She sometimes licks herself
She likes to eat tuna fish
And she loves to sleep
At night Cloud can see very well
Cloud has soft white fur
And she has a quiet purr.

Kenneth Ou (7)
The Glasgow Academy Dairsie, Glasgow

Flamingos

Flamingos are pink
They are so slow
Long, pink necks, tall like giraffes
Soft, pink feathers
Big, long beak
They fly in flocks
Their name means flame
Funny flamingos.

Eilidh Reid
The Glasgow Academy Dairsie, Glasgow

Ralphie The Playful Dog

He barks if he does not get attention
He is a very playful puppy
He loves it when his master gives him
a biscuit
He is very clean and loves going for walks
He is Ralphie.

Sebastian Carmichael (7)

The Glasgow Academy Dairsie, Glasgow

Alfie The Dog

Alfie likes to eat our food
He jumps and barks at Stella
When Dad leaves he scratches the door
He likes going to Loch Lomond
He likes to swim and get wet!

Dominic Murray (6)
The Glasgow Academy Dairsie, Glasgow

The Enormous Crocodile Has A Good Idea

The enormous crocodile creeps around
the river
The enormous crocodile has a good idea
The enormous crocodile creeps out of
the river
The enormous crocodile has a good idea

The enormous crocodile creeps into
the jungle
The enormous crocodile has a good idea
The enormous crocodile creeps around
the jungle
The enormous crocodile has a good idea

The enormous crocodile bumps into
an animal
The enormous crocodile has a good idea

The enormous crocodile said,
'It is Muggle Wump'
The enormous crocodile has a good idea

The enormous crocodile spies a juicy child
The enormous crocodile has a good idea
The enormous crocodile eats the juicy child
The enormous crocodile has a
big, fat tummy.

Rosie Eleanor Fletcher (7)
Tong Primary School, Isle Of Lewis

The Weird Noise

One day I heard a weird noise
Coming from my room
I didn't know what to do
Will I run, will I go see what it was?
I ran upstairs and into my room
And saw the enormous crocodile
His skin was as bumpy as a scrunch up
piece of paper
I ran outside into the woods and
climbed a tree
He snapped the tree, it fell into the swamp
I landed on his back
I was scared, what shall I do?
I've got it, jump, 1, 2, 3
He never saw me, I ran into my house
Locked the door...
Snap! Snap!

Daniel France (6)
Tong Primary School, Isle Of Lewis

Bad Naughty Monkey

Swing round, round and round
Until you fall onto the ground
Climb, climb up very high
Snap, snap went the branches
I saw the monkey
He threw the bananas in my mouth
He swung as fast as a flash
I thought he was a bully
He went to the top of the tree
'Hahahahaha,' he yelled
Swing round, round and round
Until you fall onto the ground
Climb, climb up very high.

Dylan MacDonald (7)
Tong Primary School, Isle Of Lewis

The Foul And Filthy Fiend

The enormous crocodile is as big as a
double-decker bus
He has sharp teeth
He bites through the trees
He is a foul and filthy fiend
His eyes glow like lantern
He makes a sound like this,
snap, snap, snap!
The enormous crocodile is coming
out of the river
The enormous crocodile is as big as the
Leaning Tower of Pisa.

Leah Macritchie (7)
Tong Primary School, Isle Of Lewis

The Scared Roly Poly Bird

When the Roly Poly Bird was in his tall tree
He saw the enormous crocodile
He looked out, he was like a chicken
He was like a scared monkey
He was like a scared octopus
He was liked a scared rhino!
His red wings are like a sunset
The Roly Poly Bird has a blue back
like the sky.

Joe Murray (7)
Tong Primary School, Isle Of Lewis

Sshhh! Crocodile!

Tiptoe, tiptoe
I can see a crocodile and he is sleeping

Tiptoe, tiptoe
I can see a crocodile and his
eyes are opening

Tiptoe, tiptoe
I can see a crocodile, here he comes!

Tiptoe, tiptoe
I can see a crocodile... *snap!*

David Finlayson (8)
Tong Primary School, Isle Of Lewis

Colourful Bird

When the Roly Poly Bird
Was going to eat some berries
She saw the enormous crocodile behind her
She shouted out the window
'The enormous crocodile is going to
eat you up!'
Her wings are red like a heart
Her back is as thin as a thick branch.

Amelia Mackay (6)
Tong Primary School, Isle Of Lewis

Cute Bird

Once upon a time there
Was a bird called Roly Poly Bird
He liked berries
His fur is like a pillow
His beak is as spiky as a drill
His eyes are as glowy as grapes
He makes a noise, it sounds like
This... *tweet, tweet, tweet!*

Ruben Matheson (8)
Tong Primary School, Isle Of Lewis

The Roly Poly Bird

The Roly Poly Bird turned and turned and
turned around
The Roly Poly Bird likes to fly above the sky
He is as muddy as a crocodile in the mud
The Roly Poly Bird likes berries to eat
He is as big as a humongous crocodile.

Johan Tynan (7)
Tong Primary School, Isle Of Lewis

The Enormous Crocodile

The crocodile always eats children
And he has scary teeth
He went into their house
And he went *snap, snap!*
And his name is the Enormous Crocodile
He lives in a swamp and it is dark.

Jayden Pidcock (7)
Tong Primary School, Isle Of Lewis

The Big Monkey

One day I heard a noise coming from the
sitting room
Bang, bang, bang
It was the gigantic monkey, Muggle Wump
The monkey is a monster monkey
And he is as fat as a pig!

Jayden Maciver (7)
Tong Primary School, Isle Of Lewis

Hippo

He is very strong
Is he nice?
Pops out when people are loud
Out when people are noisy
People love them
Opens his mouth and shows his teeth
Sometimes they do different things
Missing their baby cub
Is he in the water?
See his big eyes.

Marcus Miller (5)
Torphichen Primary School, Bathgate

Funny Kangaroo

K angaroos are mean
A re not nice
N aughty
G rumpy
A mazing jumps
R unning very fast
O pens its pouch for joey
O ver the bush he goes.

Martin Miller (5)
Torphichen Primary School, Bathgate

Jaguar Sharp

J umps
A nts tickle the jaguar
G iant teeth
U nder the long grass
A mazing colour
R uns through the long grass.

Lilly Campbell (6)
Torphichen Primary School, Bathgate

Monkeys

M onkeys are crazy
O n a tree
N ibbles bananas
K ing at climbing
E ats ants
Y ells at each other.

Alison Baird (6)

Torphichen Primary School, Bathgate

Koala

K ind to people
O n a branch enjoying leaves
A mazing
L ovely and cuddly
A mazing at climbing.

Finn McMorrow (6)

Torphichen Primary School, Bathgate

Tigers

T ricky to find

I s fast

G rowly

E xtra sharp claws

R uns fast

S leepy tigers.

Layla Rose Thomson (6)

Torphichen Primary School, Bathgate

Cheeky Monkey

Monkeys are cheeky
Monkeys are really cute
Monkeys are intelligent
Extremely long arms.

Libby Fisher (6)
Torphichen Primary School, Bathgate

Untitled

Flamingoes are pink
Flamingoes are out
Flamingoes eat leaves
Flamingoes sleep.

Summer Dunsmore (5)
Torphichen Primary School, Bathgate

Orange Squirrel

Cute, fluffy, fast
The orange squirrel is on the brown tree
and going to jump
Gobbles hard, fresh nuts
Happy because it's fluffy
As scruffy as a werewolf
Climbing tall, brown trees
It likes nuts and twigs
I like it because it is fluffy.

Ollie Saw (6)
Watlington Community Primary School, King's Lynn

The Happy Cat

Fluffy, whiskey, cuddly
In a small, little, comfy basket the cat lives
It eats crunchy, yummy cat food
I feel happy about this animal because it is
so cute and cuddly
It's as big as a mouse
It likes to run in the garden and catch
frightened mice.

Naomi Gelder (6)
Watlington Community Primary School, King's Lynn

Dancing Dalmation

Cute, speedy, cuddly
The Dalmatian runs into the house
like a flash
Scrunching yummy, tasty meat
Licking everybody
Speedy like a flash
Ruining all the pretty flowers
Running like the wind into the white kitchen
To eat yummy dog food.

Imogen Coote (6)
Watlington Community Primary School, King's Lynn

Robot Dog

Purple, yellow, hard
Underneath the sea lives a robot dog in an
underwater house
Crunches humans, sharks, snakes,
pythons, fish
Happy because it protects me
As huge as a fierce dragon
Charging up
It likes to play around.

Dylan Whiting (7)
Watlington Community Primary School, King's Lynn

The Bloodsucking Tarantula

Scary, slimy, hairy
In a big, brown tree
Is a big bloodsucking tarantula
Gobbles up anything helpless
I feel crazy because of its hair
It sucks as much blood as a vampire
Sucking blood from people every day.

Rhys Loveday (6)
Watlington Community Primary School, King's Lynn

The Tiger And The Elephant

Fast, fluffy, bloody teeth
The golden tiger hides in the golden sun
All of the other animals hide because
they are scared
As loud as an elephant
His footsteps are as big as
a lion's footsteps.

Harry Richard Gorringe (6)
Watlington Community Primary School, King's Lynn

A Happy Cute Big Owl

White, squeaky, soft
It lives in a tall, long, faraway tree
It eats crunchy, big mice
I feel happy to have a good owl
My owl is kind to me
My owl goes to the sky and my owl
flies in the sky.

Erin-Ruby Patricia Cooke (6)
Watlington Community Primary School, King's Lynn

The Playful Puppy

Fluffy, brown, small
In the kennel the puppy was sleeping
Crunches lovely dog food
Happy because I can play with it
As fluffy as a pillow
It runs around in the back garden.

Libby Hope Johnson (6)
Watlington Community Primary School, King's Lynn

The Zebra

Fluffy, kind, cute
In the meadow the zebra runs to
yummy fresh grass
The zebra eats juicy grass
The zebra is fast like a cheetah
The zebra is running into a grey tree.

Ava Faith Brooks (6)
Watlington Community Primary School, King's Lynn

The Big Fluffy Lion

Fierce, huge, spooky
Beside the tree the scary lion sleeps
Eats fresh meat
Scared because it could kill me
As soft as a teddy bear
Running and eating in the trees.

Alfie Summers (6)

Watlington Community Primary School, King's Lynn

Terrifying Terrific Tiger

Big, fast, princely
In the jungle the tiger lives
Gobbles big pieces of meat
It's longer than a panther
It's hungry and roaring through the jungle.

Harrison Cannon (6)
Watlington Community Primary School, King's Lynn

Mean Crocodile

Snappy, mean, silent
In the deep, dark river the mean crocodile
Gobbles up helpless dolphins
As bumpy as a bamboo stick
Snapping through the forest.

Finlay Dix (6)
Watlington Community Primary School, King's Lynn

Giraffe

Kind, ginormous, friendly
Tall above the leafy trees
Munching the sweet, crunchy leaves
Swaying like a flag in the wind
Running fast as a train.

Maisie Baker (6)
Watlington Community Primary School, King's Lynn

Playful Panda

Cute, fluffy, huge
It lives in the jungle in a tall tree
It eats crunchy bamboo
It's fluffy like a cloud
Walking on her four paws.

Macy Jordan (6)
Watlington Community Primary School, King's Lynn

The Big Pup

Fluffy, cute, woof
Inside the soft, loving house
Pup is sleeping
Licking his bone
Tugging the rope
Running away.

Samuel Mills (6)

Watlington Community Primary School, King's Lynn

Spider

Red, black and mean
In the deep, dark cave
There lurks a big tarantula
As squishy as a pillow
As stinky as a skunk.

Leo Sillis (6)
Watlington Community Primary School, King's Lynn

Fish

Wet, slimy, cute
Deep in the blue sea
Munch his food
Frightened
Squashy as a pillow
Slips and swims.

Benjamin Buck (6)
Watlington Community Primary School, King's Lynn

Tiny Cat

Tiny, little, cute
On the bed
It likes to eat tiny mice
Soft like a cushion
Chasing its tail.

Isabelle Pearman (6)
Watlington Community Primary School, King's Lynn

Shark

A shark is long
The shark swims in the water
He eats fish
It hides behind rocks.

Theo Sanderson (6)
Watlington Community Primary School, King's Lynn

Young Writers Information

We hope you have enjoyed reading this book – and that you will continue to in the coming years.

If you're a young writer who enjoys reading and creative writing, or the parent of an enthusiastic poet or story writer, do visit our website www.youngwriters.co.uk. Here you will find free competitions, workshops and games, as well as recommended reads, a poetry glossary and our blog.

If you would like to order further copies of this book, or any of our other titles give us a call or visit **www.youngwriters.co.uk**.

Young Writers, Remus House, Coltsfoot Drive, Peterborough, PER2 9BF (01733) 890066

info@youngwriters.co.uk